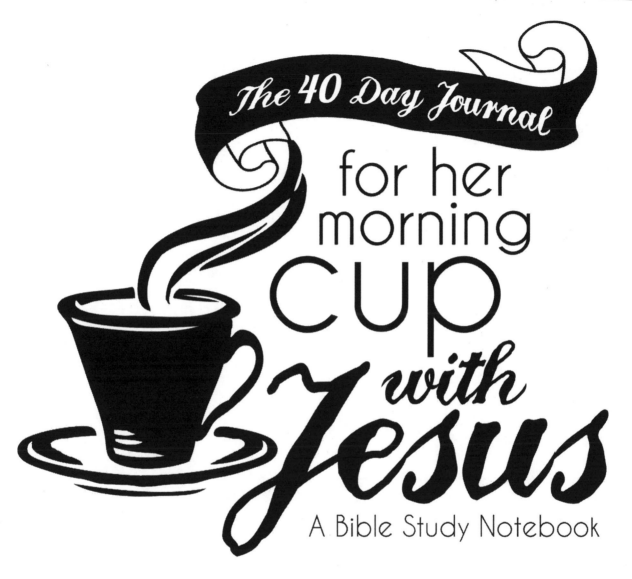

The 40 Day Journal
for her morning cup with Jesus
A Bible Study Notebook

written & designed by Shalana Frisby
COPYRIGHT 2017. ALL RIGHTS RESERVED.
www.123JournalIt.com

More information at: www.123journalit.com

First Printing: April 2017
1 2 3 Journal It Publishing

ISBN-13: 978-0-9986183-4-0

this journal
belongs to:

How to use this journal:

SIT, SIP, & SAVOR
God's holy word every single morning.

During the time it takes to finish your morning cup of favorite coffee or tea, soak up some encouragement for your entire day. Start off the right way... with your Bible open, your heart ready, and your mind focused on what matters most.

1. Fill your morning cup.
2. Open your Bible.
3. Fill your heart.
Repeat daily.

what is on my mind right now?

_____

_____

_____

_____

_____

 *my focus list* for today:

one word to describe my mood this day:

○ ....

○ ....

○ ....

○ ....

○ ....

Psst... A gentle reminder to focus on changing you & not the entire world today. YOU are the light! (Matt. 5:14-16)

...ponder...write...doodle...draw...

list words or names of praise for the Lord:

1) ....

2) ....

3) ....

4) ....

5) ....

what needs to be left at Jesus' feet today?

_____
_____
_____
_____
_____
_____
_____
_____
_____
_____
_____
_____
_____
_____
_____
_____
_____

one thing to be grateful to the Lord for this day:

Psst... The Lord loves you deeply. Yes, you! (Romans 5:8)
Praise HIM today & bring your cares to HIM. (Phil. 4:6)

thoughts on my Bible
reading for this day:

book, chapters, & verses:

_____
_____
_____
_____
_____
_____
_____
_____
_____
_____
_____
_____

Psst... Don't have anything in mind to read today?
Open your Bible to *Luke 1:39-56*.

my favorite scripture
from today's reading:

....
....
....
....
....
....
....
....
....

one way to apply it
to my life today:

....
....
....
....
....

share the good news of Jesus:
Who can I tell today & how will I do it?

...ponder...write...doodle...draw...

_____
_____
_____
_____
_____
_____
_____
_____
_____
_____
_____
_____
_____
_____
_____
_____
_____
_____
_____
_____
_____

what is on my mind right now?

today's date:

_____

_____

_____

_____

_____

my focus list for today:

○ ....

....

○ ....

....

○ ....

....

○ ....

....

○ ....

....

Psst... A gentle reminder to focus on changing you & not the entire world today. YOU are the light! (Matt. 5:14-16)

one word to describe my mood this day:

...ponder...write...doodle...draw...

list words or names
of praise for the Lord:

1) ....

2) ....

3) ....

4) ....

5) ....

one thing
to be grateful
to the Lord
for this day:

what needs to be left
at Jesus' feet today?

_____

_____

_____

_____

_____

_____

_____

_____

_____

_____

_____

_____

_____

_____

_____

_____

_____

Psst... The Lord loves you deeply. Yes, you! (Romans 5:8)
Praise HIM today & bring your cares to HIM. (Phil. 4:6)

thoughts on my Bible
reading for this day:

book, chapters, & verses:

_____

_____

_____

_____

_____

_____

_____

_____

_____

_____

_____

_____

Psst... Don't have anything in mind to read today?
Open your Bible to *Isaiah 9:6-7*.

my favorite scripture
from today's reading:

....

....

....

....

....

....

....

....

....

....

one way to apply it
to my life today:

....

....

....

....

....

....

share the good news of Jesus:
Who can I tell today & how will I do it?

...ponder...write...doodle...draw...

what is on my mind right now?

_____
_____
_____
_____
_____

my focus list for today:

○ ....
○ ....
○ ....
○ ....
○ ....
....

Psst... A gentle reminder to focus on changing you & not the entire world today. YOU are the light! (Matt. 5:14-16)

one word to describe my mood this day:

...ponder...write...doodle...draw...

15

list words or names
of praise for the Lord:

1) ....

2) ....

3) ....

4) ....

5) ....

what needs to be left
at Jesus' feet today?

_____
_____
_____
_____
_____
_____
_____
_____
_____
_____
_____
_____
_____
_____
_____
_____
_____
_____
_____
_____

one thing
to be grateful
to the Lord
for this day:

Psst... The Lord loves you deeply. Yes, you! (Romans 5:8)
Praise HIM today & bring your cares to HIM. (Phil. 4:6)

thoughts on my Bible
reading for this day:

> book, chapters, & verses:

_____

_____

_____

_____

_____

_____

_____

_____

_____

_____

_____

Psst... Don't have anything in mind to read today?
Open your Bible to *Matthew 5:13-16.*

my favorite scripture
from today's reading:

....

....

....

....

....

....

....

....

....

one way to apply it
to my life today:

....

....

....

....

....

....

share the good news of Jesus:
Who can I tell today & how will I do it?

...ponder...write...doodle...draw

what is on my mind right now?

_____
_____
_____
_____
_____

 *my focus list* for today:

one word to describe my mood this day:

- ◯ . . . .
- ◯ . . . .
- ◯ . . . .
- ◯ . . . .
- ◯ . . . .

Psst... A gentle reminder to focus on changing you & not the entire world today. YOU are the light! (Matt. 5:14-16)

...ponder...write...doodle...draw...

list words or names of praise for the Lord:

1) ....

2) ....

3) ....

4) ....

5) ....

one thing to be grateful to the Lord for this day:

what needs to be left at Jesus' feet today?

_____
_____
_____
_____
_____
_____
_____
_____
_____
_____
_____
_____
_____
_____
_____

Psst... The Lord loves you deeply. Yes, you! (Romans 5:8)
Praise HIM today & bring your cares to HIM. (Phil. 4:6)

thoughts on my Bible
reading for this day:

book, chapters, & verses:

_____
_____
_____
_____
_____
_____
_____
_____
_____
_____
_____

Psst... Don't have anything in mind to read today?
Open your Bible to *Lamentations 3:19-33.*

my favorite scripture
from today's reading:

....
....
....
....
....
....
....
....
....
....

one way to apply it
to my life today:

....
....
....
....
....
....

share the good news of Jesus:
Who can I tell today & how will I do it?

ponder...write...doodle...draw

what is on my mind right now?

 today's date:

_____

_____

_____

_____

_____

my focus list for today:

○ ....

○ ....

○ ....

○ ....

○ ....

....

Psst... A gentle reminder to focus on changing you & not the entire world today. YOU are the light! (Matt. 5:14-16)

one word to describe my mood this day:

...ponder...write...doodle...draw...

23

list words or names
of praise for the Lord:

1) ....

2) ....

3) ....

4) ....

5) ....

what needs to be left
at Jesus' feet today?

_____
_____
_____
_____
_____
_____
_____
_____
_____
_____
_____
_____
_____
_____
_____
_____
_____

one thing
to be grateful
to the Lord
for this day:

Psst... The Lord loves you deeply. Yes, you! (Romans 5:8)
Praise HIM today & bring your cares to HIM. (Phil. 4:6)

thoughts on my Bible
reading for this day:

> book, chapters, & verses:

_____

_____

_____

_____

_____

_____

_____

_____

_____

_____

_____

_____

Psst... Don't have anything in mind to read today?
Open your Bible to *Matthew 12:33-37*.

my favorite scripture
from today's reading:

....

....

....

....

....

....

....

....

....

....

one way to apply it
to my life today:

....

....

....

....

....

....

share the good news of Jesus:
Who can I tell today & how will I do it?

ponder...write...doodle...draw

what is on my mind right now?

_____

_____

_____

_____

_____

 *my focus list* for today:

one word to describe my mood this day:

○ ....

○ ....

○ ....

○ ....

○ ....

....

Psst... A gentle reminder to focus on changing you & not the entire world today. YOU are the light! (Matt. 5:14-16)

...ponder...write...doodle...draw...

27

list words or names
of praise for the Lord:

1) ....

2) ....

3) ....

4) ....

5) ....

what needs to be left
at Jesus' feet today?

_____
_____
_____
_____
_____
_____
_____
_____
_____
_____
_____
_____
_____
_____
_____
_____
_____
_____

one thing
to be grateful
to the Lord
for this day:

Psst... The Lord loves you deeply. Yes, you! (Romans 5:8)
Praise HIM today & bring your cares to HIM. (Phil. 4:6)

28

thoughts on my Bible
reading for this day:

book, chapters, & verses:

_____
_____
_____
_____
_____
_____
_____
_____
_____
_____
_____
_____

Psst... Don't have anything in mind to read today?
Open your Bible to *Ecclesiastes 3:9-15.*

my favorite scripture
from today's reading:

....
....
....
....
....
....
....
....
....
....

one way to apply it
to my life today:

....
....
....
....
....
....

share the good news of Jesus:
Who can I tell today & how will I do it?

ponder...write...doodle...draw

what is on my
mind right now?

_____

_____

_____

_____

_____

my focus list
for today:

○ ....

○ ....

○ ....

○ ....

○ ....

....

Psst... A gentle reminder to focus on changing you & not the entire world today. YOU are the light! (Matt. 5:14-16)

one word to describe
my mood this day:

...ponder...write...doodle...draw...

list words or names of praise for the Lord:

1) ....

2) ....

3) ....

4) ....

5) ....

what needs to be left at Jesus' feet today?

_____

_____

_____

_____

_____

_____

_____

_____

_____

_____

_____

_____

_____

_____

_____

_____

_____

_____

_____

one thing to be grateful to the Lord for this day:

Psst... The Lord loves you deeply. Yes, you! (Romans 5:8)
Praise HIM today & bring your cares to HIM. (Phil. 4:6)

thoughts on my Bible
reading for this day:

> book, chapters, & verses:

_____
_____
_____
_____
_____
_____
_____
_____
_____
_____
_____

Psst... Don't have anything in mind to read today?
Open your Bible to *Matthew 7:24-27*.

my favorite scripture
from today's reading:

....
....
....
....
....
....
....
....
....

one way to apply it
to my life today:

....
....
....
....
....
....

share the good news of Jesus:
Who can I tell today & how will I do it?

ponder...write...doodle...draw

what is on my mind right now?

_____

_____

_____

_____

_____

my focus list for today:

◯ ....

◯ ....

◯ ....

◯ ....

◯ ....

....

Psst... A gentle reminder to focus on changing you & not the entire world today. YOU are the light! (Matt. 5:14-16)

one word to describe my mood this day:

...ponder...write...doodle...draw...

35

list words or names
of praise for the Lord:

1) ....

2) ....

3) ....

4) ....

5) ....

what needs to be left
at Jesus' feet today?

_____

_____

_____

_____

_____

_____

_____

_____

_____

_____

_____

_____

_____

_____

_____

_____

_____

one thing
to be grateful to the Lord for this day:

Psst... The Lord loves you deeply. Yes, you! (Romans 5:8)
Praise HIM today & bring your cares to HIM. (Phil. 4:6)

thoughts on my Bible
reading for this day:

book, chapters, & verses:

_____
_____
_____
_____
_____
_____
_____
_____
_____
_____
_____

Psst... Don't have anything in mind to read today?
Open your Bible to *Micah 4:6-7.*

my favorite scripture
from today's reading:

....
....
....
....
....
....
....
....
....
....

one way to apply it
to my life today:

....
....
....
....
....
....

share the good news of Jesus:
Who can I tell today & how will I do it?

ponder...write...doodle...draw

what is on my mind right now?

_____
_____
_____
_____
_____

my focus list for today:

○ ....
○ ....
○ ....
○ ....
○ ....

Psst... A gentle reminder to focus on changing you & not the entire world today. YOU are the light! (Matt. 5:14-16)

one word to describe my mood this day:

...ponder...write...doodle...draw...

list words or names of praise for the Lord:

1) ....

2) ....

3) ....

4) ....

5) ....

what needs to be left at Jesus' feet today?

_____
_____
_____
_____
_____
_____
_____
_____
_____
_____
_____
_____
_____
_____
_____
_____

one thing to be grateful to the Lord for this day:

Psst... The Lord loves you deeply. Yes, you! (Romans 5:8)
Praise HIM today & bring your cares to HIM. (Phil. 4:6)

thoughts on my Bible
reading for this day:

book, chapters, & verses:

_____

_____

_____

_____

_____

_____

_____

_____

_____

_____

_____

_____

Psst... Don't have anything in mind to read today?
Open your Bible to *Matthew 12:7-8* and then *Hosea 6:4-7*.

my favorite scripture
from today's reading:

....

....

....

....

....

....

....

....

....

one way to apply it
to my life today:

....

....

....

....

....

....

share the good news of Jesus:
Who can I tell today & how will I do it?

ponder...write...doodle...draw

_____
_____
_____
_____
_____
_____
_____
_____
_____
_____
_____
_____
_____
_____
_____
_____
_____
_____
_____
_____
_____

what is on my mind right now?

_____

_____

_____

_____

_____

my focus list for today:

○ ....
....

○ ....
....

○ ....
....

○ ....
....

○ ....
....

Psst... A gentle reminder to focus on changing you & not the entire world today. YOU are the light! (Matt. 5:14-16)

one word to describe my mood this day:

...ponder...write...doodle...draw...

list words or names
of praise for the Lord:

1) ....

2) ....

3) ....

4) ....

5) ....

one thing
to be grateful
to the Lord
for this day:

what needs to be left
at Jesus' feet today?

_____
_____
_____
_____
_____
_____
_____
_____
_____
_____
_____
_____
_____
_____
_____
_____

Psst... The Lord loves you deeply. Yes, you! (Romans 5:8)
Praise HIM today & bring your cares to HIM. (Phil. 4:6)

thoughts on my Bible
reading for this day:

> book, chapters, & verses:

_____

_____

_____

_____

_____

_____

_____

_____

_____

_____

Psst... Don't have anything in mind to read today?
Open your Bible to _Luke 15:8-10._

my favorite scripture
from today's reading:

....
....
....
....
....
....
....
....
....

one way to apply it
to my life today:

....
....
....
....
....
....

share the good news of Jesus:
Who can I tell today & how will I do it?

ponder...write...doodle...draw

what is on my
mind right now?

_____

_____

_____

_____

_____

_____

my focus list
for today:

one word to describe
my mood this day:

○ ....

○ ....

○ ....

○ ....

○ ....

Psst... A gentle reminder to focus on changing you & not the entire world today. YOU are the light! (Matt. 5:14-16)

...ponder...write...doodle...draw...

list words or names of praise for the Lord:

1) ....

2) ....

3) ....

4) ....

5) ....

what needs to be left at Jesus' feet today?

_____
_____
_____
_____
_____
_____
_____
_____
_____
_____
_____
_____
_____
_____
_____
_____
_____
_____

one thing to be grateful to the Lord for this day:

Psst... The Lord loves you deeply. Yes, you! (Romans 5:8)
Praise HIM today & bring your cares to HIM. (Phil. 4:6)

thoughts on my Bible
reading for this day:

book, chapters, & verses:

_____
_____
_____
_____
_____
_____
_____
_____
_____
_____

Psst... Don't have anything in mind to read today?
Open your Bible to *Daniel 9*.

my favorite scripture
from today's reading:

....
....
....
....
....
....
....
....
....
....

one way to apply it
to my life today:

....
....
....
....
....
....

share the good news of Jesus:
Who can I tell today & how will I do it?

ponder...write...doodle...draw

what is on my mind right now?

_____

_____

_____

_____

_____

my focus list for today:

one word to describe my mood this day:

○ . . . .

○ . . . .

○ . . . .

○ . . . .

○ . . . .

Psst... A gentle reminder to focus on changing you & not the entire world today. YOU are the light! (Matt. 5:14-16)

...ponder...write...doodle...draw...

list words or names
of praise for the Lord:

1) ....

2) ....

3) ....

4) ....

5) ....

one thing
to be grateful
to the Lord
for this day:

what needs to be left
at Jesus' feet today?

_____
_____
_____
_____
_____
_____
_____
_____
_____
_____
_____
_____
_____
_____
_____
_____
_____

Psst... The Lord loves you deeply. Yes, you! (Romans 5:8)
Praise HIM today & bring your cares to HIM. (Phil. 4:6)

thoughts on my Bible
reading for this day:

book, chapters, & verses:

_____

_____

_____

_____

_____

_____

_____

_____

_____

_____

Psst... Don't have anything in mind to read today?
Open your Bible to *Micah 7:1-7.*

my favorite scripture
from today's reading:

....

....

....

....

....

....

....

....

one way to apply it
to my life today:

....

....

....

....

....

....

share the good news of Jesus:
Who can I tell today & how will I do it?

...ponder...write...doodle...draw...

what is on my mind right now?

_____
_____
_____
_____
_____

 *my focus list* for today:

one word to describe my mood this day:

○ ....
○ ....
○ ....
○ ....
○ ....
....

Psst... A gentle reminder to focus on changing you & not the entire world today. YOU are the light! (Matt. 5:14-16)

...ponder...write...doodle...draw...

list words or names
of praise for the Lord:

1) ....

2) ....

3) ....

4) ....

5) ....

what needs to be left
at Jesus' feet today?

_____
_____
_____
_____
_____
_____
_____
_____
_____
_____
_____
_____
_____
_____
_____
_____

one thing
to be grateful
to the Lord
for this day:

Psst... The Lord loves you deeply. Yes, you! (Romans 5:8)
Praise HIM today & bring your cares to HIM. (Phil. 4:6)

thoughts on my Bible
reading for this day:

> book, chapters, & verses:

_____

_____

_____

_____

_____

_____

_____

_____

_____

_____

_____

_____

Psst... Don't have anything in mind to read today?
Open your Bible to *Matthew 4:1-11.*

my favorite scripture
from today's reading:

....

....

....

....

....

....

....

....

....

one way to apply it
to my life today:

....

....

....

....

....

....

share the good news of Jesus:
Who can I tell today & how will I do it?

...ponder...write...doodle...draw...

what is on my mind right now?

_____

_____

_____

_____

_____

 *my focus list* for today:

one word to describe my mood this day:

⭘ ....

⭘ ....

⭘ ....

⭘ ....

⭘ ....

Psst... A gentle reminder to focus on changing you & not the entire world today. YOU are the light! (Matt. 5:14-16)

...ponder...write...doodle...draw...

list words or names
of praise for the Lord:

1) ....

2) ....

3) ....

4) ....

5) ....

one thing
to be grateful
to the Lord
for this day:

what needs to be left
at Jesus' feet today?

_____
_____
_____
_____
_____
_____
_____
_____
_____
_____
_____
_____
_____
_____
_____
_____
_____
_____
_____

Psst... The Lord loves you deeply. Yes, you! (Romans 5:8)
Praise HIM today & bring your cares to HIM. (Phil. 4:6)

thoughts on my Bible
reading for this day:

book, chapters, & verses:

_____

_____

_____

_____

_____

_____

_____

_____

_____

_____

Psst... Don't have anything in mind to read today?
Open your Bible to *Matthew 7:14-23*.

my favorite scripture
from today's reading:

....

....

....

....

....

....

....

....

....

one way to apply it
to my life today:

....

....

....

....

....

....

share the good news of Jesus:
Who can I tell today & how will I do it?

ponder...write...doodle...draw

what is on my mind right now?

_____

_____

_____

_____

_____

 *my focus list* for today:

one word to describe my mood this day:

○ ....

○ ....

○ ....

○ ....

○ ....

....

Psst... A gentle reminder to focus on changing you & not the entire world today. YOU are the light! (Matt. 5:14-16)

...ponder...write...doodle...draw...

list words or names
of praise for the Lord:

1) ....

2) ....

3) ....

4) ....

5) ....

one thing
to be grateful
to the Lord
for this day:

what needs to be left
at Jesus' feet today?

_____
_____
_____
_____
_____
_____
_____
_____
_____
_____
_____
_____
_____
_____
_____
_____
_____
_____

Psst... The Lord loves you deeply. Yes, you! (Romans 5:8)
Praise HIM today & bring your cares to HIM. (Phil. 4:6)

thoughts on my Bible
reading for this day:

> book, chapters, & verses:

_____
_____
_____
_____
_____
_____
_____
_____
_____
_____
_____

Psst... Don't have anything in mind to read today?
Open your Bible to *Psalm 109:21-31*.

my favorite scripture
from today's reading:

....
....
....
....
....
....
....
....
....
....

one way to apply it
to my life today:

....
....
....
....
....
....

share the good news of Jesus:
Who can I tell today & how will I do it?

ponder...write...doodle...draw

what is on my mind right now?

_____
_____
_____
_____
_____

my focus list for today:

○ ....
○ _____
○ _____
○ _____
○ _____
....

Psst... A gentle reminder to focus on changing you & not the entire world today. YOU are the light! (Matt. 5:14-16)

one word to describe my mood this day:

...ponder...write...doodle...draw...

list words or names
of praise for the Lord:

1) ....

2) ....

3) ....

4) ....

5) ....

what needs to be left
at Jesus' feet today?

_____

_____

_____

_____

_____

_____

_____

_____

_____

_____

_____

_____

_____

_____

_____

_____

_____

one thing
to be grateful
to the Lord
for this day:

Psst... The Lord loves you deeply. Yes, you! (Romans 5:8)
Praise HIM today & bring your cares to HIM. (Phil. 4:6)

thoughts on my Bible
reading for this day:

book, chapters, & verses:

_____
_____
_____
_____
_____
_____
_____
_____
_____
_____

Psst... Don't have anything in mind to read today?
Open your Bible to *Matthew 12:46-50.*

my favorite scripture
from today's reading:

....
....
....
....
....
....
....
....
....
....

one way to apply it
to my life today:

....
....
....
....
....
....

share the good news of Jesus:
Who can I tell today & how will I do it?

....ponder...write...doodle...draw....

what is on my mind right now?

_____

_____

_____

_____

_____

 *my focus list* for today:

one word to describe my mood this day:

○ ....

○ ....

○ ....

○ ....

○ ....

Psst... A gentle reminder to focus on changing you & not the entire world today. YOU are the light! (Matt. 5:14-16)

...ponder...write...doodle...draw...

71

list words or names
of praise for the Lord:

1) ....

2) ....

3) ....

4) ....

5) ....

one thing
to be grateful to the Lord for this day:

what needs to be left
at Jesus' feet today?

_____
_____
_____
_____
_____
_____
_____
_____
_____
_____
_____
_____
_____
_____
_____

Psst... The Lord loves you deeply. Yes, you! (Romans 5:8)
Praise HIM today & bring your cares to HIM. (Phil. 4:6)

thoughts on my Bible
reading for this day:

book, chapters, & verses:

_____

_____

_____

_____

_____

_____

_____

_____

_____

_____

Psst... Don't have anything in mind to read today?
Open your Bible to *Exodus 4:10-17*.

my favorite scripture
from today's reading:

....

....

....

....

....

....

....

....

....

one way to apply it
to my life today:

....

....

....

....

....

....

share the good news of Jesus:
Who can I tell today & how will I do it?

ponder...write...doodle...draw

what is on my mind right now?

_____
_____
_____
_____
_____

my focus list for today:

one word to describe my mood this day:

○ ....
○ ....
○ ....
○ ....
○ ....

Psst... A gentle reminder to focus on changing you & not the entire world today. YOU are the light! (Matt. 5:14-16)

...ponder...write...doodle...draw...

list words or names
of praise for the Lord:

1) ....

2) ....

3) ....

4) ....

5) ....

what needs to be left
at Jesus' feet today?

_____
_____
_____
_____
_____
_____
_____
_____
_____
_____
_____
_____
_____
_____
_____
_____

one thing
to be grateful
to the Lord
for this day:

Psst... The Lord loves you deeply. Yes, you! (Romans 5:8)
Praise HIM today & bring your cares to HIM. (Phil. 4:6)

thoughts on my Bible
reading for this day:

book, chapters, & verses:

_____
_____
_____
_____
_____
_____
_____
_____
_____
_____
_____

Psst... Don't have anything in mind to read today?
Open your Bible to *Luke 7:18-28*.

my favorite scripture
from today's reading:

....
....
....
....
....
....
....
....
....
....

one way to apply it
to my life today:

....
....
....
....
....
....

share the good news of Jesus:
Who can I tell today & how will I do it?

...ponder...write...doodle...draw

what is on my mind right now?

_____

_____

_____

_____

_____

 *my focus list* for today:

one word to describe my mood this day:

○ ....

○ ....

○ ....

○ ....

○ ....

Psst... A gentle reminder to focus on changing you & not the entire world today. YOU are the light! (Matt. 5:14-16)

...ponder...write...doodle...draw...

list words or names of praise for the Lord:

1) ....

2) ....

3) ....

4) ....

5) ....

what needs to be left at Jesus' feet today?

_____
_____
_____
_____
_____
_____
_____
_____
_____
_____
_____
_____
_____
_____
_____
_____
_____

one thing to be grateful to the Lord for this day:

Psst... The Lord loves you deeply. Yes, you! (Romans 5:8)
Praise HIM today & bring your cares to HIM. (Phil. 4:6)

thoughts on my Bible
reading for this day:

book, chapters, & verses:

_____

_____

_____

_____

_____

_____

_____

_____

_____

_____

Psst... Don't have anything in mind to read today?
Open your Bible to *Isaiah 55:6-9.*

my favorite scripture
from today's reading:

....

....

....

....

....

....

....

....

....

one way to apply it
to my life today:

....

....

....

....

....

....

share the good news of Jesus:
Who can I tell today & how will I do it?

ponder...write...doodle...draw

what is on my mind right now?

_____

_____

_____

_____

_____

 *my focus list* for today:

one word to describe my mood this day:

○ ....

○ ....

○ ....

○ ....

○ ....

....

Psst... A gentle reminder to focus on changing you & not the entire world today. YOU are the light! (Matt. 5:14-16)

...ponder...write...doodle...draw...

list words or names
of praise for the Lord:

1) ....

2) ....

3) ....

4) ....

5) ....

one thing
to be grateful
to the Lord
for this day:

what needs to be left
at Jesus' feet today?

_____

_____

_____

_____

_____

_____

_____

_____

_____

_____

_____

_____

_____

_____

_____

_____

_____

Psst... The Lord loves you deeply. Yes, you! (Romans 5:8)
Praise HIM today & bring your cares to HIM. (Phil. 4:6)

thoughts on my Bible
reading for this day:

book, chapters, & verses:

_____

_____

_____

_____

_____

_____

_____

_____

_____

_____

_____

Psst... Don't have anything in mind to read today?
Open your Bible to *Matthew 8:23-27*.

my favorite scripture
from today's reading:

....

....

....

....

....

....

....

....

....

one way to apply it
to my life today:

....

....

....

....

....

....

share the good news of Jesus:
Who can I tell today & how will I do it?

...ponder...write...doodle...draw...

what is on my mind right now?

_____

_____

_____

_____

_____

 *my focus list* for today:

one word to describe my mood this day:

○ ....

○ ....

○ ....

○ ....

○ ....

Psst... A gentle reminder to focus on changing you & not the entire world today. YOU are the light! (Matt. 5:14-16)

...ponder...write...doodle...draw...

list words or names
of praise for the Lord:

1) ....

2) ....

3) ....

4) ....

5) ....

one thing
to be grateful
to the Lord
for this day:

what needs to be left
at Jesus' feet today?

_____

_____

_____

_____

_____

_____

_____

_____

_____

_____

_____

_____

_____

_____

_____

_____

_____

_____

_____

Psst... The Lord loves you deeply. Yes, you! (Romans 5:8)
Praise HIM today & bring your cares to HIM. (Phil. 4:6)

thoughts on my Bible
reading for this day:

> book, chapters, & verses:

_____

_____

_____

_____

_____

_____

_____

_____

_____

Psst... Don't have anything in mind to read today?
Open your Bible to *Isaiah 29:13 and then Mark 7:5-9.*

my favorite scripture
from today's reading:

....

....

....

....

....

....

....

....

....

....

one way to apply it
to my life today:

....

....

....

....

....

....

share the good news of Jesus:
Who can I tell today & how will I do it?

...ponder...write...doodle...draw...

what is on my mind right now?

_____

_____

_____

_____

_____

my focus list for today:

one word to describe my mood this day:

○ ....

○ ....

○ ....

○ ....

○ ....

....

Psst... A gentle reminder to focus on changing you & not the entire world today. YOU are the light! (Matt. 5:14-16)

...ponder...write...doodle...draw...

91

list words or names
of praise for the Lord:

1) ....

2) ....

3) ....

4) ....

5) ....

one thing
to be grateful
to the Lord
for this day:

what needs to be left
at Jesus' feet today?

_____
_____
_____
_____
_____
_____
_____
_____
_____
_____
_____
_____
_____
_____
_____
_____
_____
_____
_____

Psst... The Lord loves you deeply. Yes, you! (Romans 5:8)
Praise HIM today & bring your cares to HIM. (Phil. 4:6)

thoughts on my Bible
reading for this day:

book, chapters, & verses:

_____
_____
_____
_____
_____
_____
_____
_____
_____
_____
_____
_____

Psst... Don't have anything in mind to read today?
Open your Bible to *Ecclesiastes 4:9-11*.

my favorite scripture
from today's reading:

....
....
....
....
....
....
....
....
....

one way to apply it
to my life today:

....
....
....
....
....
....

share the good news of Jesus:
Who can I tell today & how will I do it?

what is on my mind right now?

_____
_____
_____
_____
_____
_____

 *my focus list* for today:

○ ....
○ ....
○ ....
○ ....
○ ....

Psst... A gentle reminder to focus on changing you & not the entire world today. YOU are the light! (Matt. 5:14-16)

one word to describe my mood this day:

...ponder...write...doodle...draw...

95

list words or names
of praise for the Lord:

1) ....

2) ....

3) ....

4) ....

5) ....

what needs to be left
at Jesus' feet today?

_____
_____
_____
_____
_____
_____
_____
_____
_____
_____
_____
_____
_____
_____
_____
_____
_____
_____

one thing
to be grateful
to the Lord
for this day:

Psst... The Lord loves you deeply. Yes, you! (Romans 5:8)
Praise HIM today & bring your cares to HIM. (Phil. 4:6)

thoughts on my Bible reading for this day:

book, chapters, & verses:

_____
_____
_____
_____
_____
_____
_____
_____
_____
_____
_____

Psst... Don't have anything in mind to read today?
Open your Bible to *Acts 2:42-47*.

my favorite scripture from today's reading:

....
....
....
....
....
....
....
....
....

one way to apply it to my life today:

....
....
....
....
....
....

share the good news of Jesus:
Who can I tell today & how will I do it?

ponder...write...doodle...draw

what is on my mind right now?

_____

_____

_____

_____

_____

my focus list for today:

one word to describe my mood this day:

- ◯ ....
- ◯ ....
- ◯ ....
- ◯ ....
- ◯ ....

Psst... A gentle reminder to focus on changing you & not the entire world today. YOU are the light! (Matt. 5:14-16)

...ponder...write...doodle...draw...

list words or names of praise for the Lord:

1) ....

2) ....

3) ....

4) ....

5) ....

what needs to be left at Jesus' feet today?

_____
_____
_____
_____
_____
_____
_____
_____
_____
_____
_____
_____
_____
_____
_____
_____
_____

one thing to be grateful to the Lord for this day:

Psst... The Lord loves you deeply. Yes, you! (Romans 5:8)
Praise HIM today & bring your cares to HIM. (Phil. 4:6)

thoughts on my Bible
reading for this day:

book, chapters, & verses:

_____
_____
_____
_____
_____
_____
_____
_____
_____
_____
_____

Psst... Don't have anything in mind to read today?
Open your Bible to *Matthew 18:10-14.*

my favorite scripture
from today's reading:

....
....
....
....
....
....
....
....
....
....

one way to apply it
to my life today:

....
....
....
....
....
....

share the good news of Jesus:
Who can I tell today & how will I do it?

...ponder...write...doodle...draw...

what is on my mind right now?

_____

_____

_____

_____

_____

 *my focus list* for today:

○ ....

○ ....

○ ....

○ ....

○ ....

Psst... A gentle reminder to focus on changing you & not the entire world today. YOU are the light! (Matt. 5:14-16)

one word to describe my mood this day:

...ponder...write...doodle...draw...

list words or names
of praise for the Lord:

1) ....

2) ....

3) ....

4) ....

5) ....

what needs to be left
at Jesus' feet today?

_____
_____
_____
_____
_____
_____
_____
_____
_____
_____
_____

one thing
to be grateful
to the Lord
for this day:

_____
_____
_____
_____

Psst... The Lord loves you deeply. Yes, you! (Romans 5:8)
Praise HIM today & bring your cares to HIM. (Phil. 4:6)

thoughts on my Bible
reading for this day:

book, chapters, & verses:

_____
_____
_____
_____
_____
_____
_____
_____
_____
_____
_____

Psst... Don't have anything in mind to read today?
Open your Bible to *Psalm 119:103-105*.

my favorite scripture
from today's reading:

....
....
....
....
....
....
....
....
....
....

one way to apply it
to my life today:

....
....
....
....
....
....

share the good news of Jesus:
Who can I tell today & how will I do it?

ponder...write...doodle...draw

what is on my mind right now?

_____

_____

_____

_____

_____

my focus list for today:

- ○ ....
- ○ ....
- ○ ....
- ○ ....
- ○ ....

Psst... A gentle reminder to focus on changing you & not the entire world today. YOU are the light! (Matt. 5:14-16)

one word to describe my mood this day:

...ponder...write...doodle...draw...

107

list words or names of praise for the Lord:

1) ....

2) ....

3) ....

4) ....

5) ....

one thing to be grateful to the Lord for this day:

what needs to be left at Jesus' feet today?

_____
_____
_____
_____
_____
_____
_____
_____
_____
_____
_____
_____
_____
_____
_____
_____

Psst... The Lord loves you deeply. Yes, you! (Romans 5:8)
Praise HIM today & bring your cares to HIM. (Phil. 4:6)

thoughts on my Bible
reading for this day:

book, chapters, & verses:

_____
_____
_____
_____
_____
_____
_____
_____
_____
_____

Psst... Don't have anything in mind to read today?
Open your Bible to *Matthew 3:13-17*.

my favorite scripture
from today's reading:

....
....
....
....
....
....
....
....
....

one way to apply it
to my life today:

....
....
....
....
....
....

share the good news of Jesus:
Who can I tell today & how will I do it?

...ponder...write...doodle...draw...

what is on my mind right now?

my focus list for today:

○ ....
○ ....
○ ....
○ ....
○ ....
....

Psst... A gentle reminder to focus on changing you & not the entire world today. YOU are the light! (Matt. 5:14-16)

one word to describe my mood this day:

...ponder...write...doodle...draw...

list words or names
of praise for the Lord:

1) ....

2) ....

3) ....

4) ....

5) ....

one thing
to be grateful to the Lord for this day:

what needs to be left
at Jesus' feet today?

_____

_____

_____

_____

_____

_____

_____

_____

_____

_____

_____

_____

_____

_____

_____

_____

_____

Psst... The Lord loves you deeply. Yes, you! (Romans 5:8)
Praise HIM today & bring your cares to HIM. (Phil. 4:6)

thoughts on my Bible
reading for this day:

book, chapters, & verses:

_____

_____

_____

_____

_____

_____

_____

_____

_____

_____

_____

Psst... Don't have anything in mind to read today?
Open your Bible to *Proverbs 23:19-25*.

my favorite scripture
from today's reading:

....

....

....

....

....

....

....

....

....

one way to apply it
to my life today:

....

....

....

....

....

share the good news of Jesus:
Who can I tell today & how will I do it?

ponder...write...doodle...draw

what is on my mind right now?

my focus list for today:

○ ....
○ ....
○ ....
○ ....
○ ....
....

Psst... A gentle reminder to focus on changing you & not the entire world today. YOU are the light! (Matt. 5:14-16)

one word to describe my mood this day:

...ponder...write...doodle...draw...

115

list words or names
of praise for the Lord:

1) ....

2) ....

3) ....

4) ....

5) ....

what needs to be left
at Jesus' feet today?

_____
_____
_____
_____
_____
_____
_____
_____
_____
_____
_____
_____
_____
_____
_____
_____

one thing
to be grateful
to the Lord
for this day:

Psst... The Lord loves you deeply. Yes, you! (Romans 5:8)
Praise HIM today & bring your cares to HIM. (Phil. 4:6)

thoughts on my Bible
reading for this day:

book, chapters, & verses:

_____
_____
_____
_____
_____
_____
_____
_____
_____
_____
_____
_____

Psst... Don't have anything in mind to read today?
Open your Bible to *Psalm 2*.

my favorite scripture
from today's reading:

....
....
....
....
....
....
....
....
....

one way to apply it
to my life today:

....
....
....
....
....
....

share the good news of Jesus:
Who can I tell today & how will I do it?

...ponder...write...doodle...draw...

what is on my mind right now?

_____

_____

_____

_____

_____

 *my focus list* for today:

one word to describe my mood this day:

○ ....

○ ....

○ ....

○ ....

○ ....

....

Psst... A gentle reminder to focus on changing you & not the entire world today. YOU are the light! (Matt. 5:14-16)

...ponder...write...doodle...draw...

119

list words or names
of praise for the Lord:

1) ....

2) ....

3) ....

4) ....

5) ....

what needs to be left
at Jesus' feet today?

_____

_____

_____

_____

_____

_____

_____

_____

_____

_____

_____

_____

_____

_____

_____

_____

_____

one thing
to be grateful
to the Lord
for this day:

Psst... The Lord loves you deeply. Yes, you! (Romans 5:8)
Praise HIM today & bring your cares to HIM. (Phil. 4:6)

thoughts on my Bible
reading for this day:

book, chapters, & verses:

_____

_____

_____

_____

_____

_____

_____

_____

_____

_____

_____

Psst... Don't have anything in mind to read today?
Open your Bible to *Psalm 3*.

my favorite scripture
from today's reading:

....

....

....

....

....

....

....

....

....

....

one way to apply it
to my life today:

....

....

....

....

....

....

share the good news of Jesus:
Who can I tell today & how will I do it?

...ponder...write...doodle...draw...

what is on my mind right now?

_____

_____

_____

_____

_____

my focus list for today:

one word to describe my mood this day:

- ○ ....
- ○ ....
- ○ ....
- ○ ....
- ○ ....

Psst... A gentle reminder to focus on changing you & not the entire world today. YOU are the light! (Matt. 5:14-16)

...ponder...write...doodle...draw...

123

list words or names
of praise for the Lord:

1) ....

2) ....

3) ....

4) ....

5) ....

one thing
to be grateful
to the Lord
for this day:

what needs to be left
at Jesus' feet today?

_____

_____

_____

_____

_____

_____

_____

_____

_____

_____

_____

_____

_____

_____

_____

_____

Psst... The Lord loves you deeply. Yes, you! (Romans 5:8)
Praise HIM today & bring your cares to HIM. (Phil. 4:6)

thoughts on my Bible
reading for this day:

book, chapters, & verses:

_____
_____
_____
_____
_____
_____
_____
_____
_____
_____
_____

Psst... Don't have anything in mind to read today?
Open your Bible to *Romans 5:12-21*.

my favorite scripture
from today's reading:

....
....
....
....
....
....
....
....
....

one way to apply it
to my life today:

....
....
....
....
....

share the good news of Jesus:
Who can I tell today & how will I do it?

...ponder...write...doodle...draw...

what is on my mind right now?

_____

_____

_____

_____

_____

my focus list for today:

○ ....

○ ....

○ ....

○ ....

○ ....

Psst... A gentle reminder to focus on changing you & not the entire world today. YOU are the light! (Matt. 5:14-16)

one word to describe my mood this day:

...ponder...write...doodle...draw...

127

list words or names
of praise for the Lord:

1) ....

2) ....

3) ....

4) ....

5) ....

what needs to be left
at Jesus' feet today?

_____

_____

_____

_____

_____

_____

_____

_____

_____

_____

_____

_____

_____

_____

one thing
to be grateful
to the Lord
for this day:

Psst... The Lord loves you deeply. Yes, you! (Romans 5:8)
Praise HIM today & bring your cares to HIM. (Phil. 4:6)

thoughts on my Bible
reading for this day:

book, chapters, & verses:

_____

_____

_____

_____

_____

_____

_____

_____

_____

_____

_____

Psst... Don't have anything in mind to read today?
Open your Bible to *Matthew 14:22-36.*

my favorite scripture
from today's reading:

....

....

....

....

....

....

....

....

....

one way to apply it
to my life today:

....

....

....

....

....

....

share the good news of Jesus:
Who can I tell today & how will I do it?

ponder...write...doodle...draw

what is on my mind right now?

_____

_____

_____

_____

_____

 *my focus list* for today:

○ ....

○ ....

○ ....

○ ....

○ ....

Psst... A gentle reminder to focus on changing you & not the entire world today. YOU are the light! (Matt. 5:14-16)

one word to describe my mood this day:

...ponder...write...doodle...draw...

list words or names
of praise for the Lord:

1) ....

2) ....

3) ....

4) ....

5) ....

what needs to be left
at Jesus' feet today?

_____

_____

_____

_____

_____

_____

_____

_____

_____

_____

_____

_____

_____

_____

_____

_____

_____

_____

_____

one thing
to be grateful
to the Lord
for this day:

Psst... The Lord loves you deeply. Yes, you! (Romans 5:8)
Praise HIM today & bring your cares to HIM. (Phil. 4:6)

thoughts on my Bible
reading for this day:

book, chapters, & verses:

_____
_____
_____
_____
_____
_____
_____
_____
_____
_____
_____

Psst... Don't have anything in mind to read today?
Open your Bible to *Luke 12:4-7.*

my favorite scripture
from today's reading:

....
....
....
....
....
....
....
....
....
....

one way to apply it
to my life today:

....
....
....
....
....
....

share the good news of Jesus:
Who can I tell today & how will I do it?

ponder...write...doodle...draw

what is on my mind right now?

_____
_____
_____
_____
_____

 *my focus list* for today:

one word to describe my mood this day:

○ ....
○ ....
○ ....
○ ....
○ ....

Psst... A gentle reminder to focus on changing you & not the entire world today. YOU are the light! (Matt. 5:14-16)

...ponder...write...doodle...draw...

135

list words or names of praise for the Lord:

1) ....

2) ....

3) ....

4) ....

5) ....

what needs to be left at Jesus' feet today?

_____
_____
_____
_____
_____
_____
_____
_____
_____
_____
_____
_____
_____
_____
_____
_____

one thing to be grateful to the Lord for this day:

Psst... The Lord loves you deeply. Yes, you! (Romans 5:8)
Praise HIM today & bring your cares to HIM. (Phil. 4:6)

thoughts on my Bible
reading for this day:

book, chapters, & verses:

_____
_____
_____
_____
_____
_____
_____
_____
_____
_____
_____

Psst... Don't have anything in mind to read today?
Open your Bible to *Romans 6:1-12.*

my favorite scripture
from today's reading:

....
....
....
....
....
....
....
....
....

one way to apply it
to my life today:

....
....
....
....
....
....

share the good news of Jesus:
Who can I tell today & how will I do it?

ponder...write...doodle...draw

what is on my mind right now?

my focus list for today:

○ ....
○ ....
○ ....
○ ....
○ ....
....

Psst... A gentle reminder to focus on changing you & not the entire world today. YOU are the light! (Matt. 5:14-16)

one word to describe my mood this day:

...ponder...write...doodle...draw...

139

list words or names
of praise for the Lord:

1) ....

2) ....

3) ....

4) ....

5) ....

what needs to be left
at Jesus' feet today?

_____
_____
_____
_____
_____
_____
_____
_____
_____
_____
_____
_____
_____
_____
_____
_____
_____

one thing
to be grateful
to the Lord
for this day:

Psst... The Lord loves you deeply. Yes, you! (Romans 5:8)
Praise HIM today & bring your cares to HIM. (Phil. 4:6)

thoughts on my Bible
reading for this day:

book, chapters, & verses:

_____
_____
_____
_____
_____
_____
_____
_____
_____
_____
_____
_____

Psst... Don't have anything in mind to read today?
Open your Bible to *Genesis 3:1-13*.

my favorite scripture
from today's reading:

....
....
....
....
....
....
....
....
....

one way to apply it
to my life today:

....
....
....
....
....
....

share the good news of Jesus:
Who can I tell today & how will I do it?

ponder...write...doodle...draw

what is on my mind right now?

_____
_____
_____
_____
_____

my focus list for today:

○ ....
○ ....
○ ....
○ ....
○ ....

Psst... A gentle reminder to focus on changing you & not the entire world today. YOU are the light! (Matt. 5:14-16)

one word to describe my mood this day:

...ponder...write...doodle...draw...

list words or names
of praise for the Lord:

1) ....

2) ....

3) ....

4) ....

5) ....

one thing
to be grateful
to the Lord
for this day:

what needs to be left
at Jesus' feet today?

_____
_____
_____
_____
_____
_____
_____
_____
_____
_____
_____
_____
_____
_____
_____
_____
_____
_____
_____
_____

Psst... The Lord loves you deeply. Yes, you! (Romans 5:8)
Praise HIM today & bring your cares to HIM. (Phil. 4:6)

thoughts on my Bible
reading for this day:

book, chapters, & verses:

_____
_____
_____
_____
_____
_____
_____
_____
_____
_____
_____

Psst... Don't have anything in mind to read today?
Open your Bible to *Jonah 4:2*.

my favorite scripture
from today's reading:

....
....
....
....
....
....
....
....
....
....

one way to apply it
to my life today:

....
....
....
....
....

share the good news of Jesus:
Who can I tell today & how will I do it?

ponder...write...doodle...draw

what is on my mind right now?

_____

_____

_____

_____

_____

my focus list for today:

○ ....

○ ....

○ ....

○ ....

○ ....

Psst... A gentle reminder to focus on changing you & not the entire world today. YOU are the light! (Matt. 5:14-16)

one word to describe my mood this day:

...ponder...write...doodle...draw...

list words or names
of praise for the Lord:

1) ....

2) ....

3) ....

4) ....

5) ....

one thing
to be grateful
to the Lord
for this day:

what needs to be left
at Jesus' feet today?

_____

_____

_____

_____

_____

_____

_____

_____

_____

_____

_____

_____

_____

_____

_____

_____

_____

_____

Psst... The Lord loves you deeply. Yes, you! (Romans 5:8)
Praise HIM today & bring your cares to HIM. (Phil. 4:6)

thoughts on my Bible
reading for this day:

book, chapters, & verses:

_____
_____
_____
_____
_____
_____
_____
_____
_____
_____

Psst... Don't have anything in mind to read today?
Open your Bible to *Matthew 24:36-44.*

my favorite scripture
from today's reading:

....
....
....
....
....
....
....
....
....
....

one way to apply it
to my life today:

....
....
....
....
....
....

share the good news of Jesus:
Who can I tell today & how will I do it?

ponder...write...doodle...draw

what is on my mind right now?

my focus list for today:

◯ ....
....
◯ ....
....
◯ ....
....
◯ ....
....
◯ ....
....

Psst... A gentle reminder to focus on changing you & not the entire world today. YOU are the light! (Matt. 5:14-16)

one word to describe my mood this day:

...ponder...write...doodle...draw...

list words or names of praise for the Lord:

1) ....

2) ....

3) ....

4) ....

5) ....

what needs to be left at Jesus' feet today?

_____
_____
_____
_____
_____
_____
_____
_____
_____
_____
_____
_____
_____
_____
_____
_____
_____

Psst... The Lord loves you deeply. Yes, you! (Romans 5:8)
Praise HIM today & bring your cares to HIM. (Phil. 4:6)

one thing to be grateful to the Lord for this day:

thoughts on my Bible
reading for this day:

book, chapters, & verses:

_____

_____

_____

_____

_____

_____

_____

_____

_____

_____

_____

Psst... Don't have anything in mind to read today?
Open your Bible to *Matthew 26:1-35.*

my favorite scripture
from today's reading:

....

....

....

....

....

....

....

....

....

one way to apply it
to my life today:

....

....

....

....

....

share the good news of Jesus:
Who can I tell today & how will I do it?

153

...ponder...write...doodle...draw

what is on my mind right now?

_____

_____

_____

_____

_____

my focus list for today:

○ ....

○ ....

○ ....

○ ....

○ ....

....

Psst... A gentle reminder to focus on changing you & not the entire world today. YOU are the light! (Matt. 5:14-16)

one word to describe my mood this day:

...ponder...write...doodle...draw...

list words or names
of praise for the Lord:

1) ....

2) ....

3) ....

4) ....

5) ....

what needs to be left
at Jesus' feet today?

_____

_____

_____

_____

_____

_____

_____

_____

_____

_____

_____

_____

_____

_____

_____

_____

_____

_____

_____

one thing
to be grateful
to the Lord
for this day:

Psst... The Lord loves you deeply. Yes, you! (Romans 5:8)
Praise HIM today & bring your cares to HIM. (Phil. 4:6)

thoughts on my Bible
reading for this day:

> book, chapters, & verses:

_____
_____
_____
_____
_____
_____
_____
_____
_____
_____
_____

Psst... Don't have anything in mind to read today?
Open your Bible to *John 18:33-40 and 19:1-16.*

my favorite scripture
from today's reading:

....
....
....
....
....
....
....
....
....

one way to apply it
to my life today:

....
....
....
....
....
....

share the good news of Jesus:
Who can I tell today & how will I do it?

...ponder...write...doodle...draw...

what is on my mind right now?

_____
_____
_____
_____
_____

my focus list for today:

○ ....
....
○ ....
....
○ ....
....
○ ....
....
○ ....
....

Psst... A gentle reminder to focus on changing you & not the entire world today. YOU are the light! (Matt. 5:14-16)

one word to describe my mood this day:

...ponder...write...doodle...draw...

list words or names
of praise for the Lord:

1) ....

2) ....

3) ....

4) ....

5) ....

one thing
to be grateful
to the Lord
for this day:

what needs to be left
at Jesus' feet today?

_____

_____

_____

_____

_____

_____

_____

_____

_____

_____

_____

_____

_____

_____

_____

_____

Psst... The Lord loves you deeply. Yes, you! (Romans 5:8)
Praise HIM today & bring your cares to HIM. (Phil. 4:6)

thoughts on my Bible
reading for this day:

book, chapters, & verses:

_____
_____
_____
_____
_____
_____
_____
_____
_____
_____
_____
_____

Psst... Don't have anything in mind to read today?
Open your Bible to *John 19:17-37 and then Mark 15:16-41.*

my favorite scripture
from today's reading:

....
....
....
....
....
....
....
....
....

one way to apply it
to my life today:

....
....
....
....
....
....

share the good news of Jesus:
Who can I tell today & how will I do it?

ponder...write...doodle...draw

what is on my mind right now?

_____

_____

_____

_____

_____

my focus list for today:

- ○ ....
- ○ ....
- ○ ....
- ○ ....
- ○ ....

Psst... A gentle reminder to focus on changing you & not the entire world today. YOU are the light! (Matt. 5:14-16)

one word to describe my mood this day:

...ponder...write...doodle...draw...

list words or names
of praise for the Lord:

1) ....

2) ....

3) ....

4) ....

5) ....

what needs to be left
at Jesus' feet today?

_____
_____
_____
_____
_____
_____
_____
_____
_____
_____
_____
_____
_____
_____
_____
_____

one thing
to be grateful
to the Lord
for this day:

Psst... The Lord loves you deeply. Yes, you! (Romans 5:8)
Praise HIM today & bring your cares to HIM. (Phil. 4:6)

thoughts on my Bible
reading for this day:

book, chapters, & verses:

_____
_____
_____
_____
_____
_____
_____
_____
_____
_____
_____

Psst... Don't have anything in mind to read today?
Open your Bible to *Matthew 27:57-66 and 28:1-15.*

my favorite scripture
from today's reading:

....
....
....
....
....
....
....
....
....
....

one way to apply it
to my life today:

....
....
....
....
....
....

share the good news of Jesus:
Who can I tell today & how will I do it?

ponder...write...doodle...draw

Praise the Lord!
...you finished it...

Don't stop your daily Bible study journey now.

Keep on READING *it,* PONDERING *it,* ABSORBING *its message,* SHARING *it with others,* & APPLYING *it to your daily* LIFE.

...............all the little notes...............

..................all the little notes..................

.................all the little notes.................

...............all the little notes..................

.................all the little notes...................

.............all the little notes.............

.................all the little notes.................

.................all the little notes...................

Thank you for using one of our journals!

Our family appreciates your purchase and feedback. If you found this journal useful (hopefully a bit life-changing too), we ask you to tell a friend and consider writing a review. Our goal is to spread the good news of Jesus and inspire others to learn more about God's word...one journal at a time.

With much ♥,
The Frisby's
Stephen, Shalana & Rowynn

p.s. Check out our website for other fun journals!

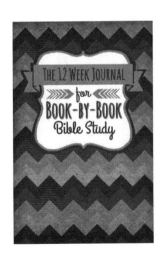  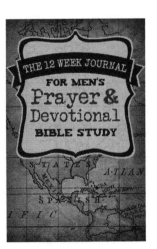 

1.2.3...journal it!

find more about us at www.123journalit.com
...self-guided DIY study books for the whole family...

98242503R00102